Theory
Workbook

Grade **8**

Written by
Anthony Crossland &
Terence Greaves

ABRSM

First published in 2000 by ABRSM (Publishing) Ltd,
a wholly owned subsidiary of ABRSM, 24 Portland Place, London W1B 1LU.

Reprinted in 2000, 2003, 2004, 2005, 2006, 2008, 2010

© 2000 by The Associated Board of the Royal Schools of Music

AB 2718

A CIP catalogue record for this book is available from The British Library.

Extracts from the following copyright works are reproduced with permission:

Walton: Symphony No. 2
Bloch: *Schelomo*
Ducas: *The Sorcerer's Apprentice*

Typeset by Musonix
Printed in Great Britain by Halstan & Co. Ltd., Amersham, Bucks.

Contents

The system of chord labelling used in this workbook is 'extended Roman'. It best identifies the sound quality of the chord and its function within the key. Please note, however, that examination candidates may use any recognised method of chord labelling, provided it presents a clear indication or a precise description of the harmony.

Introduction

This *Theory Workbook* provides straightforward information and advice about, and practice for, the Associated Board's Grade 8 theory exam papers. It focuses on the skills, knowledge and understanding that are being tested at the grade, exploring each specific element of the syllabus in some detail and providing insights into how candidates can approach their papers in a positive frame of mind and with every chance of success.

The workbook is complementary to the Board's range of related theory publications, in particular *The AB Guide to Music Theory* and *Harmony in Practice*. With all these, students will be supremely well-equipped to acquire the essential theory skills and understanding they need for their musical development in general and undertaking their Associated Board Grade 8 Theory exam in particular.

Philip Mundey
Director of Examinations

Question 1

In this question you will be asked to complete a short passage from a Baroque trio sonata for two treble instruments and basso continuo. The openings of all parts will be given and the basso continuo will be provided throughout and fully figured. You are not expected to supply a keyboard realisation of the latter, but to complete the two upper parts in accordance with the figuring. Note that, for exam purposes, short horizontal lines in the basso continuo indicate the resolution of dissonant notes, such as the resolution of suspensions, and longer lines indicate the continuation of the previous harmony. Melodic fragments may be given in the upper parts to help with your working. The passage will be in a major or minor key which is unlikely to exceed four sharps or four flats. (For figured bass see *The AB Guide to Music Theory*, Part I 8/4 and *Harmony in Practice*, 'Chord Labelling'.)

Before we consider an example, two general points need to be made:

1. To produce a good answer you must take into account not only the harmonic structure suggested by the figured bass, but also the shape and character of the two upper parts, together with the overall musical texture and style. Many students merely fill in the harmony from the figures and ignore the necessity to write a well-shaped melody featuring points of imitation, rhythmic patterns and other characteristics included in the given material.

2. You must think about the ranges of the instruments concerned (see *The AB Guide to Music Theory*, Part II, Chapters 19 and 20). Try not to confine your writing to just one narrow part of the range, but take care not to go below the bottom note of the instrument (e.g. middle C for a flute).

Sample Question 1

This was used in the 1999A Grade 8 exam paper.

Complete the violin parts in the following extract from a trio sonata by Purcell, following the figuring shown under the basso continuo.

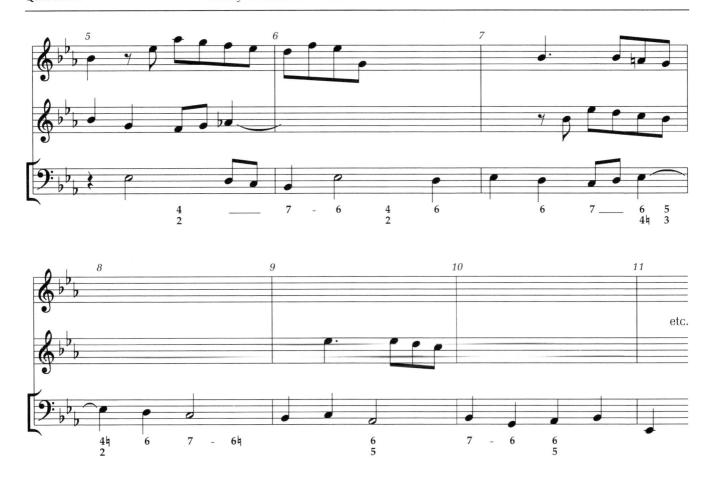

WORKING THE QUESTION

Take a moment to look at the extract and assess its character. Note any imitative or other significant feature in what is given.

This is a lively piece for two violins (therefore the lowest note is G below the stave) in the key of E♭ major. The opening Violin 1 figure is used for the entry of Violin 2, and (though note values are sometimes different) it forms the main melodic contour of the basso continuo. It also reappears in bar 7 (Violin 1) and bar 9 (Violin 2), and is therefore of considerable structural importance. The fragment of melody given in bar 7, Violin 2, has also been used in bar 5, Violin 1, and so this figure may also assume importance in the working.

Next, go through the extract and, on the basso continuo stave or on a separate sheet of manuscript paper, pencil in note-heads to indicate the chords implied above each of the figures where a working is required. (Where no figures are given, $\frac{5}{3}$ chords should be inserted.) This will show you the harmonic structure of the whole passage and provide the main framework for the construction of your added melodies.

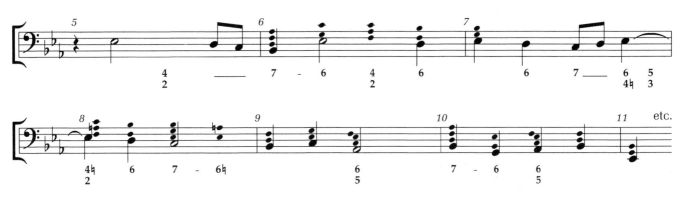

Now look at bars 6 and 7. You will see that the given material in bar 7 divides the whole extract into two, giving a short section to complete first.

Remember that your aim should be to write horizontal melodic lines, **not** merely to complete vertical harmonic beats of the bar, and here you should look first at the Violin 2 part. You will see that this begins in bar 3 as an imitation of the opening Violin 1 melody, and a glance at the harmonic framework, together with the added clue of the tie between bars 5 and 6, shows that the imitation can be continued up to the end of the phrase (the first note of bar 7). This may be pencilled in and will look like this:

Now complete the Violin 1 part of bar 6. There are no imitative precedents for this and so you are free to do as you wish, within certain limitations:

- See that your additions conform to the figuring and fill out the harmony as much as possible.

- Ensure that your added line has some melodic interest.

- Ensure that your added line is reasonably independent **rhythmically** from the other two lines.

- Retain the overall style of the passage.

Bearing in mind the above points, let us now consider bar 6.

If we wish to have as full harmony as possible we need the important note A♭ on the third crotchet beat, and on the fourth, a B♭. At the beginning of bar 7 a G is essential as it is the 3rd of the chord.

These three notes, A♭, B♭ and G, have a certain shape but, as shown below, the repeats of the G and B♭ are rather dull:

There is a real need for rhythmic independence here as both the bass and Violin 2 are moving in crotchets and minims. It would be desirable, therefore, to maintain the preceding quaver movement and possibly introduce some notes of melodic decoration, and this would also alleviate the dullness of the melodic line which we noticed above. The following would work perfectly well:

What Purcell does is to use a group of four quavers, the second of which, a C, neatly provides the remaining harmony note of the $\frac{4}{2}$ chord. This also provides a rising 3rd, nicely complementing the melodic shape in the first half of the bar. Whilst it is possible to use crotchets in all three parts at the beginning of bar 7, Purcell keeps the movement going by using two quavers – G and E♭:

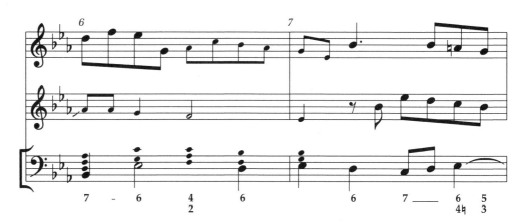

Remember that the object of the exercise is not necessarily to reproduce exactly what the composer originally wrote, and you may frequently find other options which are equally acceptable musically. The examiners do not mark this question with a copy of the original in front of them, penalising the candidate for every note which differs from it. Any answer which does not contain consecutive 5ths or octaves, or other breaches of musical grammar, and which demonstrates an awareness of the style and texture of the given material will receive due credit.

You should now check this completed section of your working for such consecutives. This is an uninteresting chore, but it really is essential. The most foolproof method is to check each line against every other line:

- Check Violin 2 with Basso Continuo.

- Check Violin 2 with Violin 1.

- Check Violin 1 with Basso Continuo.

Now complete bars 8 and 9. Although, in our working, we are thinking essentially of continuous horizontal lines, it is a good idea to divide the passage into shorter units which are easier to manage. The little figure given in the Violin 2 part at bar 9 gives us a good opportunity to complete bars 8 and 9 before going on to the end.

It is fairly clear that the musical content of these two bars will be largely governed by the two snatches of melody which appear in bar 7. The Violin 1

figure was first used at the beginning of the extract, and the Violin 2 figure appeared earlier in Violin 1, bar 5.

Consider first the Violin 1 part of bar 7. You will notice that its pitch is now the same as the Violin 2 entry (bar 3) and the first thing to do is see if the continuation of that figure (bar 4, etc.) will work here. You will see that it fits perfectly, and so it may be pencilled in as far as the first crotchet, B♭, in bar 9, as shown in the music example below.

Now look at the Violin 2 figure in bar 7 which is the same as that used in Violin 1, bar 5, but a 4th lower in pitch. We should now see if the continuation of the latter, Violin 1 bars 6–7, will fit Violin 2 bars 8–9. Again we are in luck and the notes may be added as far as the beginning of bar 9. This section is now complete and looks like this:

Check this section of your working for consecutives. After you have done this the remainder of the extract may be completed.

As we have been given a few notes of the opening figure in the Violin 2 part at bar 9, let us deal with this first. Follow what has become our standard procedure and see if the continuation of the figure (bar 2 of the extract) will fit the harmonic scheme given here. It does, even to the E♭ which will begin bar 11.

Now we need to complete the Violin 1 part from bar 9 to the end. You will remember that from bar 7 onwards we were able to give Violin 1 the same music that Violin 2 had used from bar 3 to the beginning of bar 5. This procedure can continue right up to the end of the extract, since bars 5–7 of Violin 2 will fit perfectly into bars 9–11 of Violin 1.

Check this section for consecutives, then rub out the note-heads which you pencilled in to show chords implied by the figuring.

Printed on the facing page is the complete passage with the music that Purcell wrote.

You may be surprised at the comparative ease with which the question was completed, and there is no doubt that the musical ideas interlocked logically and naturally. Not all questions can be completed quite so smoothly, and some modification of the given motifs may be necessary at times. (Even here the stepwise descent of Violin 1 at bar 3 had to be changed to a leap of a 3rd in bar 5, Violin 2.) But once you are able to work out how the various musical ideas can fit together and, above all, when you are able to **think and work in horizontal musical lines**, this question should not cause you undue worry; these skills are readily acquired with a little practice.

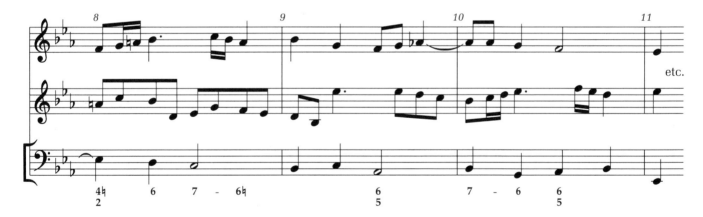

▶ **SOME GENERAL POINTS**

- It does not necessarily follow that all notes for the bars you have to complete can be obtained from the given music. You may have to supply some original material, although you should try to relate this to the given passages whenever possible. Candidates who fail to appreciate this will sometimes use the given musical figures to produce harmony that does not correspond with the figured bass. This is why you should always write in the note-heads to remind yourself of the notes needed for each chord and ensure that your added lines always conform to these.

- In a three-part texture such as this, it is obviously not always possible to include all the harmony notes suggested by the figuring, and you may have to be guided at times by the melodic shape of the lines. The 3rd of the chord should normally be present, as should any notes actually designated by the figuring (such as 7, 4, 2, etc.), though there may be occasions when this is not possible and, in practice, the keyboard continuo player would fill in essential notes not played by the two solo instruments.

• The 7th from the bass should be prepared on the preceding chord in the same part and should resolve (also in the same part) down a step. Failure to do this usually stems from thinking vertically in chords, rather than in melodic lines; the unsatisfactory result should be readily apparent to the ear. Bad usage of the 7th in bar 8 of our example is given below:

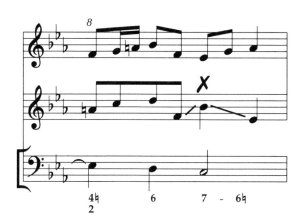

Similarly, the dissonant interval of a 4th should normally resolve to a 3rd in the same part, and all suspensions should resolve in the same part (normally down by a step). Leading notes should rise by a step to the tonic.

• In these instrumental passages crossing of the upper parts can happen quite frequently, and may well be desirable (if not essential) to realise the figuring correctly or to make proper use of an imitative musical figure. Large melodic leaps are also commonplace; they usually occur on one of the main beats of the bar. An example may be seen in the extract we have worked in bar 9 of the Violin 2 part.

• A rest or rests may appear in the given part of this question. It is, of course, perfectly in order (and sometimes advantageous) for you to use them in your completed sections, especially when they form part of a significant musical figure, or act as punctuation marks between phrases or sections of the passage. **They must, however, always be used for a proper musical purpose**, never as an easy option to cover the ground quickly. Consider the following opening:

You will see that the Oboe 2 part has an imitative figure which has been delayed by two bars. Once the passage is underway, it is highly unlikely that such a large gap will recur, and you should not assume that the opening two-bar rest sets any musical precedent for your working.

Sample Question 2

Let us look at another short passage. Here you are given the basso continuo and the opening of the two upper parts.

Complete the violin parts in the following extract from a trio sonata by Vivaldi, following the figuring shown under the basso continuo.

WORKING THE QUESTION

The given material immediately shows that this extract has a totally different texture and character from the first example, and its completion therefore presents us with different problems.

This is adagio, in a minor key, and with a bass line that maintains steady quaver movement throughout: the main crotchet beats are turned into repeated quavers and given added interest by interval leaps, usually of an octave. Above this the two violins have lyrical melodies in which, as the given opening indicates, suspensions are going to form an important feature. (See *Harmony in Practice*, Chapter 14 'Dissonant and prepared decoration – the suspension', for some help in dealing with the suspension.)

You will also see that no additional fragments of music have been inserted to offer any clues to assist the working: there is merely a succession of empty bars. In this situation you should turn for help to what *is* provided by the given material, and here two particular aspects are likely to be of value:

1. The figuring of the bass line. You will see that virtually every bar begins with 4–3, indicating a sequence of 4–3 suspensions.

2.   The given opening of Violin 2 suggests an imitation of Violin 1 which might be continued. This may well lead to opportunities for 'leapfrogging', in which each part, in turn, supplies material for the other.

Before we see how these two factors may assist our working, it is advisable, as before, to write down the chords implied by the figures. In extracts such as this, where the basso continuo line is quite full, it is best to use a separate sheet of manuscript paper. Here, the implied chords have been written in the treble clef, but you could use the bass clef if preferred.

We now know which notes are going to be essential to our working; from the character of the piece and the texture of the given violin openings, it is unlikely that many inessential notes will be required.

Remember that every bar that begins with the figuring 4–3 must have a suspended 4th at the beginning in one of the upper parts, and that this note must be prepared on the last beat of the previous bar, tied over the bar-line, and must then resolve, **in the same part**, on to a 3rd – either plainly or in a decorated manner such as appears in bar 2 of the Violin 1 part.

The obvious first step is to put such a decorated resolution into the Violin 2 part of bar 3. This leads to a crotchet F on the last beat of the bar, which is the note needed for the next 4–3 suspension at the beginning of bar 4:

No alternative is possible, as the Violin 1 part is given for the end of bar 3 and is clearly leading up towards a C rather than preparing a suspension.

It seems likely that the Violin 2 suspension into bar 4 will have a similar decorated resolution, producing an E at the end of the bar. This will not serve for the next suspension, which must therefore take place in the Violin 1 part. Write this in, with a Bb at the end of bar 4, tied over the bar-line, resolving with its decoration on A at the end of bar 5. The section will now look like this, and the 'leap-frogging' between the two violin parts mentioned earlier is apparent:

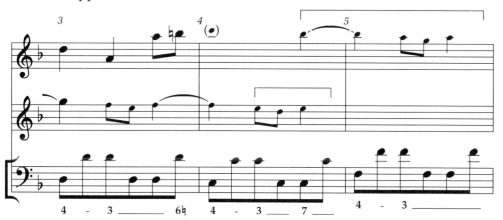

✳ *Note the effectiveness of building up your working by first putting in those parts of the texture which are determined by what is given in the melodic lines and figured bass.*

Look now at the suspension at the beginning of bar 6. This must be an F, prepared at the end of the previous bar, and it therefore must be written into the Violin 2 part since Violin 1 is already committed to an A at the end of bar 5. The usual decorated resolution will fit perfectly well and so this should now be written in.

Now apply the same procedure for the beginning of bar 7. Here the suspended note will be a G, with a decorated resolution on to an F, and prepared by a crotchet G at the end of the preceding bar. This must be in the Violin 1 part and may be put into the working:

You can see from the bass figuring that no suspension is implied at the beginning of bar 8 and that bars 8 and 9 will consist of a perfect cadence in the tonic key of D minor.

The best procedure now is to go back and complete the blank sections of the violin parts and then devise a suitable cadence figure for the end. In filling these gaps you should attempt to:

- maintain the steady musical flow, consisting mostly of crotchets and minims;

- maintain reasonable melodic interest in the individual parts;

- produce as complete harmony as you can, in accordance with the given figuring.

With these three factors in mind, let us turn to our skeleton working as it stands at present.

Your plan of action should be as follows:

Bar 4, Violin 1   We have already noticed that a note C is implied at the beginning of the bar. A note G on the second beat would complete the harmony well, and if both C and G were written as crotchets they would echo effectively the two crotchets and falling 4th interval at the start of the previous bar.

Bar 5, Violin 2   A note F at the beginning of the bar is implied by the leading note E at the end of bar 4. A note C on the second beat would again complete the harmony well, and if these two notes were written as crotchets our pattern of two crotchets and a falling 4th would be maintained.

Bar 6, Violin 1   A similar procedure may be used here, with a crotchet G followed by a crotchet C. Though the falling interval this time is a 5th, the overall shape is similar to the two previous bars and gives cohesion to the passage.

Bar 7, Violin 2 We cannot continue the pattern here, as moving up to an F at the beginning of the bar would give an unpleasant clash of the suspended G against its note of resolution. The other two notes of a D minor chord are available to us, and as a D is already in the bass line, the obvious choice would be an A, which from the harmonic point of view could be a minim. Looking at the figuring for the last beat of the bar, you will see that a 5th above the bass is required as well as a 7th. This chord would normally be figured with just a 7, implying the use of a 3rd for the other part. Here the figure 5 has been inserted to make clear that this note should be used and not the 3rd. The last note must therefore be a crotchet D. To give added movement and melodic interest, Vivaldi writes quavers D and C♯ for the second beat, producing an auxiliary-note figure in 3rds with Violin 1.

We now have just the cadence bars to consider. The harmony is extremely simple, with A major for bar 8 and D minor for bar 9, and, within the limitations of these two chords, it is simply a matter of trying to introduce some movement and melodic shape in the violin parts. An obvious starting point would be to continue the figure in 3rds which we had in the previous bar, and a descending passing-note figure in 3rds would start the bar well:

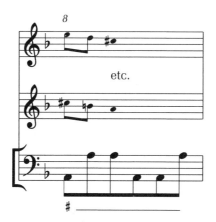

It would be possible, but rather unimaginative, for both parts to continue quaver movement in 3rds throughout the bar. A more stylish solution would be to give Violin 2 a little rhythmic independence by using a crotchet on beat 3 while Violin 1 rises to a note of anticipation on D at the very end of bar 8. The last three bars would then appear as follows. Note in bar 8 the use of the **melodic minor scale** in the two violin parts. The melodic form of the minor scale is normally preferable in these workings in order to avoid the less agreeable augmented 2nd interval between the 6th and 7th degrees of the harmonic minor scale.

This is our completed working, just one of several possible answers which should not be regarded as the definitive version:

Question 1   Sample Questions

Some sample questions for you to work now follow. The first of these is longer than a typical exam question and suggestions for procedure are given, though you must supply the actual notes. For Sample Question 2 some guidance is given, whereas Sample Questions 3–8 are presented just as in an exam paper.

Complete the upper two parts in the following extracts from trio sonatas, following the figuring shown under the basso continuo.

1.   Corelli: Trio Sonata in G major, Op. 3 No. 6

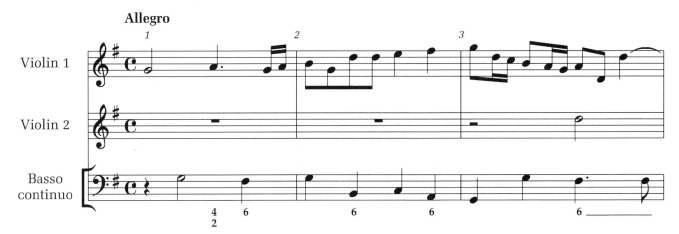

Follow these steps in your working of the question:

1. Note the key and general character of the passage.

2. Note the instruments involved and particularly the lowest notes of their range.

3. On the basso continuo stave or on manuscript paper, lightly pencil in note-heads to indicate the notes of all the chords implied by the given figuring.

4. Look at the opening figures in both violin parts, noting similarities and also the point at which they begin to differ from each other.

5. Remember the desirability of introducing some movement in either of the upper parts when the bass line has longer note values.

6. Divide the passage into conveniently sized sections which you will complete one after the other. Some sections are immediately apparent because of notes and/or rests which have been supplied. Where there are no such aids, look at the bass line for implied cadence points – here you will see one (perfect cadence in G major) halfway through bar 13. Although some movement will probably continue in the added parts, this will form a useful place to pause for further thought.

7. Proceed now with your working using the following plan:

a) Violin 1, bars 6 and 7

The rests define the end of this phrase and the tied crotchet–quaver should give a strong clue to what is expected next.

b) Violin 2, bars 6–9

Again the final given quaver in bar 6 should be of help. Note the 7 figuring under the first bass note of bar 7 – a note G must be used in one of the violin parts here, and it should be prepared in the same part on the last beat of bar 6. It should move down by a step (also in the same part) on the second beat of bar 7.

You should write original music for Violin 2 from bar 7 to bar 9, where another 7th chord has to be used.

c) Violin 1, bars 9 and 10

This should be very straightforward.

d) Violin 2, bars 11–13

Finish this section with a crotchet G (above the top line of the stave) halfway through bar 13. For the earlier part look very carefully at what was given at the end of bar 10 and beginning of bar 11. Look carefully also at the figuring for this section, remembering how the dissonances of the 4th, 9th and 7th should be prepared and resolved.

e) Violin 1, bars 11–13

A close look at the given material in the Violin 1 part of bar 11 should help you with the beginning of this section. From bar 12 you will need to supply original music but if you have achieved the correct layout for the Violin 2 part here the Violin 1 notes should not cause great difficulty.

f) Violin 1, bars 14–15

This is little more than a decorated cadence figure, and the opening of it should suggest itself automatically.

g) Violin 2, bars 13–15

Look at the figuring for the first beat of bar 14. Only one note is possible here in Violin 2, and this will also give you the last note for bar 13 and, with only a minimum of detective work (study the bass figures), the remaining notes of the section.

2.   Telemann: Trio Sonata in C minor

Note that the descending basso continuo figure from halfway through bar 2 to the end of bar 3 implies a sequence in the progression of 5ths (see *Harmony in Practice*, Chapter 9), which should be followed in the violin parts.

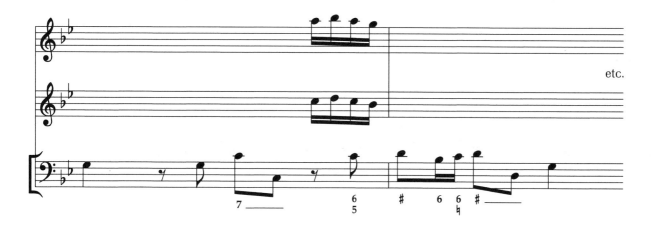

3.   Bach: Trio Sonata No. 3 in G major, BWV 1038

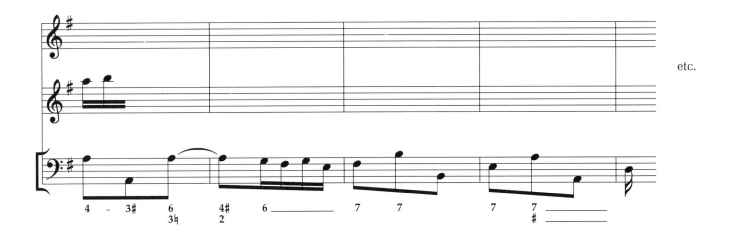

etc.

4.   Corelli: Trio Sonata in G major, Op. 3 No. 6

5.   Purcell: Trio Sonata No. 2 in F major

6.   Corelli: Trio Sonata in D major, Op. posth.

7.   Telemann: Trio Sonata in A major

8.   Corelli: Trio Sonata in B minor, Op. 3 No. 4

Question 2

This is another question that requires you to complete a passage of music, but this time without the help of a figured bass to give the harmonic frame-work. As the syllabus explains, it will be a keyboard piece and the musical style will be from a later period than the passage used in Question 1:

Completion of an outline of a short passage for keyboard. Some knowledge of the styles practised by composers from the time of Haydn onwards will be assumed.

You will therefore be dealing with keyboard textures and a more complex harmonic language, although it will not involve extreme chromaticism. In practice, the passage set will most likely be in a Classical or Romantic style – candidates will not be expected to have to use the more dissonant or rhythmically complex idioms found in some 20th-century music.

The passage will probably begin with a few complete bars of music, to give you an idea of the general texture, and, later, small fragments of music may possibly be included. You should look closely at these as they are likely to give valuable guidance towards completing the passage.

Sample Question

Complete the given outline of the following passage from *Morning Pastimes*, for piano, by Zdeněk Fibich (1850–1900).

WORKING THE QUESTION

First of all look through the passage and note:

(a) its key;

(b) its general character and structure;

(c) any implied modulations;

(d) any significant melodic or rhythmic figures in the given parts.

We can see that:

(a) The key is G major.

(b) It is a graceful, steadily flowing piece, with musical dialogue between the two hands. The phrase structure appears to be well balanced, with four phrases of four bars each. We can see, from the dates of the composer as well as the given material, that the music is composed in a simple Romantic style.

(c) There is a modulation to D major at bar 8, with a return to G major at the end of the extract.

(d) Two figures appear to have some importance; firstly, the syncopated opening melody in the left hand:

and secondly a rhythmic development of this which is seen in the right hand at bars 2–4, and which recurs later:

Having carried out this preliminary research, you need to remember two important aspects before beginning the actual work of completing the passage:

1. **Be very sure in your mind where notes (and possibly rests) are going to be needed, and where they are not.**

   This might seem obvious, but in the exam candidates frequently omit to fill up partly completed bars, especially those containing only rests. For example, in the right-hand part of bar 5 notes or rests to the value of one crotchet need to be added; similarly the left-hand part of bar 8 requires a dotted crotchet's worth of music.

2. **Look through the bars which have to be completed and note the harmony which is implied at these places. Before you begin to put in any notes, it is essential that you have a clear picture of the harmonic structure of the extract, and this should be pencilled into your working at this stage.**

   Where just treble-stave material is to be supplied, this will be governed by the harmonic implications of the bass part at that place. Where the left-hand part is needed, the right-hand line, and possibly musical devices such as sequences, may indicate the harmony. Where you have to supply music for both staves you must seek the harmony from sequences, answering phrases, or from any clues obtained from the music (especially the bass part) immediately preceding and following the section on which you are working. You are strongly advised to complete the bass line first in such places.

With these factors in mind let us return to our example and attempt to complete the harmonic skeleton.

We have already noted the main modulations, and that the structure consists of four four-bar phrases. Look now at the passages which have to be completed.

Bars 5–6 right hand
Bars 5–8 left hand

The balanced phrase structure of the extract, together with the melodic fragment at the end of bar 4 in the left hand, suggest that bar 5 will be similar to bar 1, that is centred around G major. This gives us a broad harmonic pattern for this section of G major for bars 5 and 6, D major for bar 8, and chords in bar 7 (which will be discussed later) to link the two keys. This may be pencilled into the working:

Bars 9–10 right hand
Bars 11–12 left hand

It would be helpful to consider these two sections of the third phrase together because, as we shall see, they are heavily interdependent.

The right-hand figure which links bars 8 and 9 and which is then apparently imitated in the left hand strongly suggests A minor for bar 9. The next two bars might seem complex, with the natural signs in bar 10 and the E♭ in bar 11, so let us leave these for the moment. Bar 12 is clearer with its direct suggestion of D major:

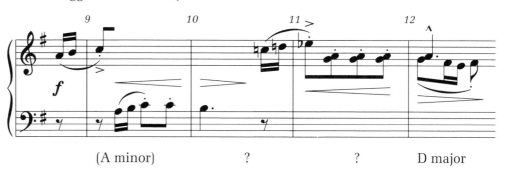

Bars 13–16 right hand
Bars 13–14 left hand

The similarity of the left-hand pair of semiquavers at the end of bar 12 to those at the beginning of the piece should be apparent, and indicate the probable re-use of the opening material at this point. We can therefore pencil in G major for bars 13 and 14. A brief transition to D major may be possible at the beginning of bar 15, while G major at the end of bar 15 leads to our final perfect cadence in the tonic key. The harmonic outline is now complete.

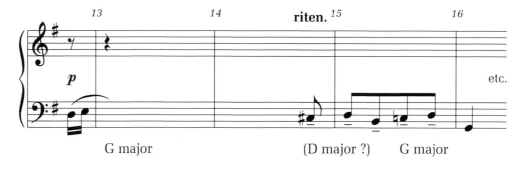

It is vital that you establish the broad harmonic outline of the extract, as shown above, before you begin working the question.

Many candidates spoil their workings by immediately filling in the notes, often using figures from other parts of the extract which are harmonically inappropriate, and whose unsuitability would have been obvious had a proper harmonic foundation first been established.

We can now begin adding the musical detail, looking first at the passage up to bar 8.

Bars 5–8 form an answering phrase to the first four bars and lead the tonality away from G major to the dominant, D major. The left-hand ending of bar 4 suggests a recurrence of the opening material which is strengthened by the quaver and crotchet rests in the right hand. Firstly, therefore, we can simply repeat the notes of the first half of the opening phrase, up to the last quaver beat of bar 2:

The next task is to supply a convincing bass part for the modulation to D major. If we look first at the corresponding place in the first phrase (bar 3) we see that four quavers were used in each hand. It would create good balance to use the same texture in bar 7. The note A would work throughout the bar, producing a $^6_4$ chord for the first half, a decorated resolution of 4–3, and a chord with an added 6th on the last quaver. But merely to repeat an A four times would be rather dull, and some variety, such as dropping an octave after the first note and then filling in the harmony by using three two-note chords, would be an improvement:

Further harmonic interest could be added by putting a G into the last left-hand chord of the bar, thus turning it into a 13th chord on A:

It remains to provide a link-note for the last quaver of bar 6. We could, of course, simply use a quaver rest, but whilst this would not be impossible it would be preferable to provide a positive link, rather than leave the left hand in mid-air, as it were, at the end of the bar. The harmony for bar 6 is G major, but to have another G in the left hand at the end of a bar which has so far had only a held G would not be very adventurous. A stronger move would be to add a B, giving the variety of an implied $\frac{6}{3}$ chord. More imaginative still would be to use a G♯, thereby suggesting a $\frac{6}{5}$ dominant 7th chord in the key of A, and the end of the phrase would then appear as follows (quaver movement has been maintained in the left hand of bar 8 by a repetition of the three-note figure used in bar 4):

This is a perfectly satisfactory completion of the phrase. What Fibich actually does is vary the harmony still more by using a secondary 7th on the third quaver of bar 7, together with a thinner left-hand texture, and he delays the move to a G♯ until the final semiquaver of bar 6, like this:

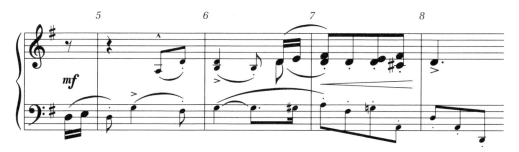

In bar 7 you can see that the harmonic progression for the four quaver beats – in the key of D – is Ic, Ib, ii^{7}b and either iiib or V^{13}, if one takes account of the strong dominant flavour provided by the bass note A. Though the earlier workings of this bar are perfectly acceptable, Fibich's version gives maximum interest to the harmony and the bass line.

We now move on to consider bars 9–12, which presently look like this:

When we were working out the broad harmonic basis for the extract, the key of A minor was suggested for bar 9, while bars 10 and 11, with their more complicated appearance, were not considered at that point. The reason is that in a well-balanced four-phrase structure, such as this, it is in the third phrase that the most harmonic movement is likely to occur. In addition, the given material in these bars suggests some imitation and perhaps sequential repetition. It may well be, therefore, that the given melodic ideas here may guide us, not only to the melodic structure of the missing sections, but also towards the harmony.

With this in mind look at the right hand of bars 9 and 10. It should be obvious that the two semiquavers–quaver figure from bars 8–9 is meant to be continued on the lines of a similar figure elsewhere: the question is, which one? You will see that similar figures are used in the right hand of bars 6–7 and 10–11, and also in the left hand of bar 9.

The last, left-hand option may be rejected straight away, as its use in the right hand would lead to an unpleasant clash on the third quaver beat of a B against a C.

The first (the right-hand figure in bars 6–7) is not only the end of a phrase, but also the end of the first half of the passage. It is most unlikely that the same figure would be used to begin the second half, and its use would again lead to unpleasant clashes between the two hands.

We are left, then, with the second right-hand option, from bars 10–11. If the notes of this figure (transposed down a minor 3rd, as the given opening of bars 8–9 indicates) are put into bars 9–10 they fit perfectly, forming an A minor chord with an added 6th in bar 9. This has a decorated resolution on to B major in bar 10, the D♯ and C♯ being implied by the naturals which are given at the end of the bar.

In working out the left hand of bars 11 and 12 it is logical to repeat the two bars we have just completed a minor 3rd higher, to form a sequence. This would mean having a quaver rest at the beginning of bar 11 and then using the left-hand melody of bars 9–10 a minor 3rd higher, beginning on middle C. This gives an added 6th chord of C minor which resolves on to D major at bar 12, thus producing a smooth link with the G major harmony which is required at bar 13:

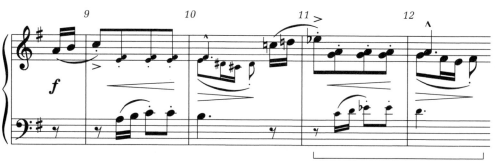

*As you have just seen, a quaver rest was needed in the left hand at the beginning of bar 11. Rests are sometimes as necessary to the completion of this question as notes, **but only when they serve a valid musical purpose**, such as to act as punctuation between two phrases or, as here, to reproduce a sequence properly. As in Question 1, they should not be used excessively or indiscriminately.*

We now have to complete the last four-bar phrase:

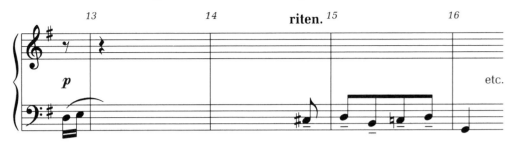

The two left-hand semiquavers at the end of bar 12, together with the right-hand rests, suggest a return of the material used at the beginning of the extract and this would be perfectly in keeping with the overall structural balance:

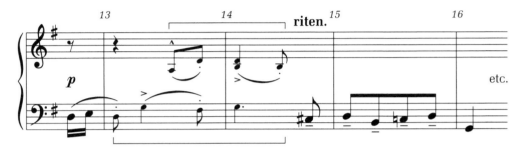

Two things now remain to be done:

1. To complete the final cadence and its approach.

2. To provide material for the last quaver beat of bar 14 which will link the two sections of the final phrase satisfactorily.

Let us look first at bars 15–16. In order to correspond well to the comparable passage at bars 7–8 a reasonably full chordal texture is indicated, whilst the familiar rhythmic pattern of ♫ | ♩♩♩♩ | ♩ would fit well. We should also bear in mind that, at the approach to a cadence, more rapid changes of chord add musical strength, and so, within the overall feel of D major – G major, other chords may be introduced to good effect in bar 15.

The first note of the bar suggests a tonic $\frac{6}{4}$ in G major which will finally resolve on to a D major $\frac{5}{3}$ chord on the last quaver beat. In between, the second quaver B implies a $\frac{6}{3}$ G major chord, whilst there are various options for the third (C♮), including a C major chord or a ii^{7}b in G major:

A wide range of chord layouts is possible: those printed at the top of the opposite page are just three examples.

We must now link the two halves of the phrase with a chord for the last quaver of bar 14. The bass has a C♯ at this point, with G major harmony on either side of it: this strongly implies some form of A major chord (the dominant of the dominant of G major). This will work well, either as a

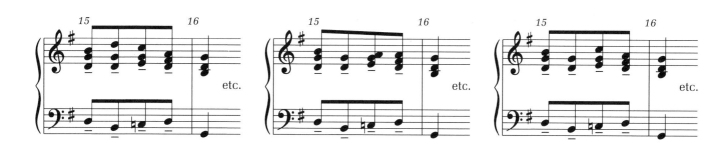

straight first inversion of A major, or as a $\frac{6}{5}$ dominant 7th in the key of D. The composer is, in fact, a little more adventurous and uses a diminished 7th chord on the C♯, repeating it as two semiquavers in order to conform to the characteristic rhythmic figure mentioned above.

Here now is the complete passage as Fibich wrote it. You will see that he uses chords of the 9th and 13th in bar 15, but these are by no means essential to a satisfactory working.

Slurs and other marks of articulation should be added throughout your own workings, following the patterns suggested in the given material.

Poco allegretto

A note about consecutive 5ths and octaves

In keyboard writing, avoidance of consecutive 5ths and octaves is less strict than in vocal writing. Octave doubling of melodies in the right- or left-hand parts occurs quite frequently, sometimes with the inclusion of the 5th (and the 3rd) to strengthen the tonal lines and musical texture.

It is recommended, for exam purposes, that the only effect you might consider is the doubling of a melody in octaves, either in the right- or left-hand parts, and then only if the given material implies such a procedure. Avoid any consecutive octaves between the top right-hand and bottom left-hand parts, and also the use of consecutive 5ths altogether.

▶ **CHECKLIST OF PROCEDURES FOR WORKING THIS QUESTION**

- Note the key, any implied modulations and, as far as you can, the harmonic basis of the passage, and pencil all these in lightly.

- Note the general character and musical texture of the passage.

- Note any significant melodic or rhythmic figures in the given material which might be used in your working.

- Note the phrase structure of the passage and pencil this in lightly.

- Fix clearly in your mind those places where you have to add material, and where you do not.

- **Look out for any changes of clef on either stave during the course of the passage. Failure to observe these will inevitably lead to inaccuracy in your working.**

- Be very sparing in your use of rests, and always see that they serve a valid musical purpose, such as the correct imitation of a given musical figure or a small punctuation of the phrase structure. It is most unlikely that long rests (such as a whole bar or more) will be called for.

- Build up the passage phrase by phrase, having the harmonic basis of each section very clear in your mind. Remember that given melodic fragments can sometimes imply harmony, as well as the opportunity to use imitation or sequence.

- In sections where you have to supply music for both staves, try to complete the bass first, unless there are special reasons (such as follow-ing a sequence or piece of imitation) for beginning with the treble stave.

- Keep an eye on the overall balance of the phrase structure, which can sometimes be helpful in suggesting the re-use of previous material.

- Remember that it is sometimes easier to work backwards from a cadence or cadence approach, towards the beginning of a phrase.

- In your practice workings be sure regularly to play over the sections as you complete them (or get someone to do this for you) so that you become accustomed to hearing what you write.

- When you have completed your working remember to add phrasing, articulation marks and any other necessary performance directions to your added sections, in accordance with those supplied in the given parts of the extract.

Question 2   Sample Questions

The following passages have been taken or adapted from works by various composers.

Complete the given outlines of the following piano pieces.

1.   T. F. Kirchner (1823–1903): No. 14 from *New Scenes of Childhood*, Op. 55

2.   Hummel (1778–1837): *Klavierschule*, No. 48

3.   Haydn: Sonata in B♭ major, Hob. XVI:17

etc.

4.   Hiller (1811–1885): *Polish Song,* Op. 117 No. 18

etc.

5.   Karganov (1858–1890): *Arabesque,* Op. 6 No. 2 (adapted)

6.   Reinecke (1824–1910): *Five Serenades for the Young,* Op. 183 (adapted)

7.   T. F. Kirchner (1823–1903): No. 11 from *Miniatures,* Op. 62

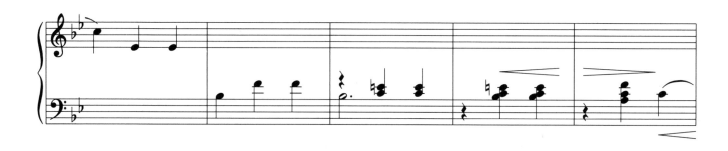

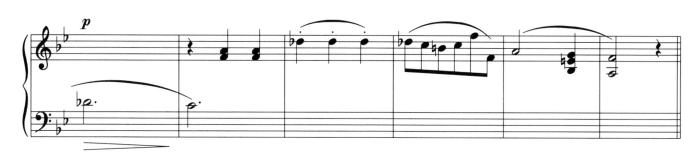

8.   Fuchs (1847–1927): *Mother tells a Story* from *Children's Pieces*, Op. 47

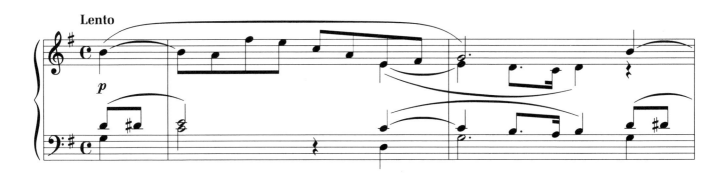

Question 3

If you have worked through Question 3 in the Grade 6 and 7 Workbooks, the melodic composition question for Grade 8 will have been prepared in many essential respects, as there are so many points in common. The main aim is still to write a melody which has good structural shape and a plausible key scheme, with a strong line coming from the use of motifs developed from the given opening. At this grade, it is even more important to adhere to the style suggested by the opening material, and to write effectively for the instrument concerned.

The question reads:

Compose a melody of not less than 12 bars using ONE of the given openings and for the given unaccompanied instrument. Continue in the same style and include appropriate performance directions. Write the complete melody on the staves below.

Modulations are not prescribed, as they were in Grade 6, but it is usually necessary to modulate at least twice (to a related key, and back to the tonic before the end) in order to produce satisfactory tonal variety in a melody of this length.

One of the melodic openings will be in a traditional style and sometimes a composer's name will be given, while the other is likely to be in a freer style, more modern in character, but not atonal. The instrument to be used in each case will be specified, and will involve the use of either bass or treble clef, with an option for alto clef when appropriate.

The task of continuing a traditional-style opening often seems at first to be the easier choice, but experience shows that students are often unable to maintain that style – they fall into the trap of continuing in their own idiom and fail to write a structured melody. Although students are not expected to produce a replica of the composer's own continuation, they must show a definite awareness of the characteristics of the appropriate style in order to produce a satisfactory working. Studying melodies from the repertoire of your own instrument or voice, particularly those you have prepared for performance, is an ideal way to appreciate the general and finer points of the style of various composers and periods. With these points firmly grasped, you will be well equipped to attempt this first option.

For the average student the apparently more daunting choice, continuing the free-style melody, is often more suitable. The style of the given opening still needs to be maintained but, because it is often freer, the continuation can also be freer. However, the continuation must still show a clear structure based on effective use of the given motif.

You do not have to limit yourself to the minimum 12 bars. In fact, the most typical length of a balanced melody is 16 bars and this offers the most satisfactory starting point in constructing a melody in either of the options.

Information about notes of melodic decoration, aspects of melody and writing for instruments will be found in Chapters 15, 18 and 19–20 respectively of *The AB Guide to Music Theory*, Part II.

Traditional-style melody

Let us concentrate on continuing a given start by Mozart.

BASSOON

WORKING THE QUESTION

First we should list the important features:

- The key is F major.

- There are two main figures:

  i)   a staccato quaver followed by a slurred trill figure with grace notes leading to a crotchet a 3rd higher, which is repeated in sequence a 3rd lower in the next bar;

  ii) a slurred semiquaver pattern of two adjacent notes repeated.

- The opening suggests Classical style.

- We are to write for bassoon.

A 16-bar plan such as the following will give a balanced structure.

Bar 1	2	3	4	5	6	7	8
Given opening 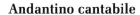			continue ♪s to complete a two-bar answering phrase	similar four-bar phrase modulating to the dominant by bar 8 (the halfway point)			

Bar 9	10	11	12	13	14	15	16
two-bar modulating sequence introducing E♭ to reach subdominant key in bar 10 then E♮ to reach tonic in bar 12 (supertonic modulation also effective in bars 9–10)				repetition of bars 1–3 in the same key will bring a sense of return and unity, and lead us to the tonic in bar 16			

A plan such as this is very useful even if it lacks detail. Many unbalanced and meandering lines with a poor sense of tonality could be avoided by such an approach. It has been applied to the version below, which overworks the main motif and lacks both rhythmic interest and style, although it has a strong sense of tonality and the phrases are balanced.

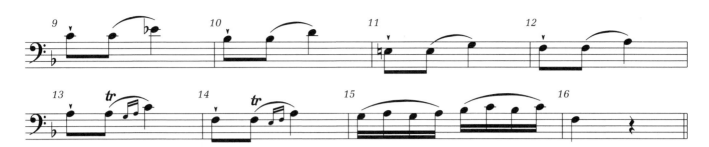

We need to use the semiquaver figure more or invent new material which will be in keeping with the style. In bar 4 we could introduce a semiquaver run down to the supertonic. Inversion of the opening motif would give variety to bars 5–6 and we could base these bars on chord vi (D minor) rather than on the tonic triad. Bar 7 would use the semiquaver figure more effectively by starting on an E and ascending to the cadence in the dominant in bar 8. An inverted form of the semiquaver figure could be used effectively for bars 9–10, which modulate to B♭ major, and in the sequence in bars 11–12. Now the exact repetition of bars 1–3 in bars 13–15 is timely and effective and the melody ends confidently in the tonic with an upward-resolving appoggiatura which matches the B♮–C in bar 8. Here are these features incorporated in a new working of the continuation:

Andantino cantabile

This is a great improvement but we could make it still more effective by introducing some more stylistic features, as in the version below. Bar 4 now includes a 'feminine ending' at the cadence which decorates the supertonic. Notice that we have added a semiquaver rest in bar 4 and a quaver rest in bar 6, to allow the player to breathe. In bar 6 we have introduced a chromatic grace note. In bar 8 the new trill emphasises the leading note of the dominant in the cadence, and again there is a rest for breathing.

Andantino cantabile

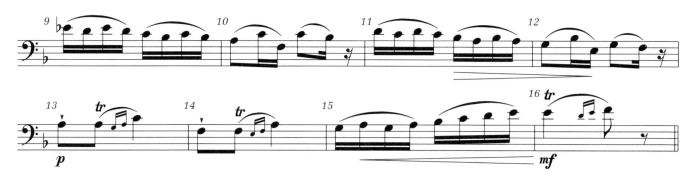

In bars 10 and 12 a new rhythmic figure introduces decorated cadences in
B♭ major and F major respectively. In the penultimate bar the semiquaver
figure is modified to lead to a trill like that at the halfway point. Dynamics
have also been added.

Now look at Mozart's original melody below, which is actually the top
line of the right-hand part for piano from the Violin Sonata, K. 379:

Andantino cantabile

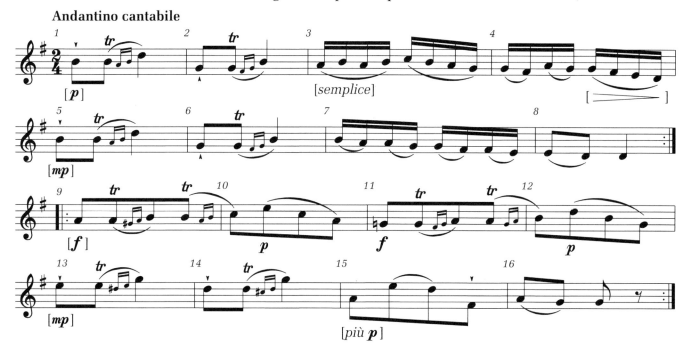

Notice the detailed phrasing, and how Mozart's sequence in bars 9–12 uses
supertonic modulation. (This can be very effective for a modulating sequence, particularly in major keys.) Bar 4 consists of a varied sequence of
bar 3, there is new material in bars 15–16, and decorated cadences in bars
8 and 16. Many melodies adopt a similar simple pattern and it would help
to study them when preparing for this option, particularly those from the
Classical and early Romantic periods by composers such as Haydn, Mozart,
Beethoven, Schubert and Weber.

Question 3   Sample Questions

The following openings can be worked for various instruments and in
various clefs to extend their usefulness, but remember that you will have to
write for the specified instrument in the actual exam.

**Compose melodies of not less than 12 bars using the following openings
and for the given unaccompanied instruments. Continue in the same style
and include appropriate performance directions.**

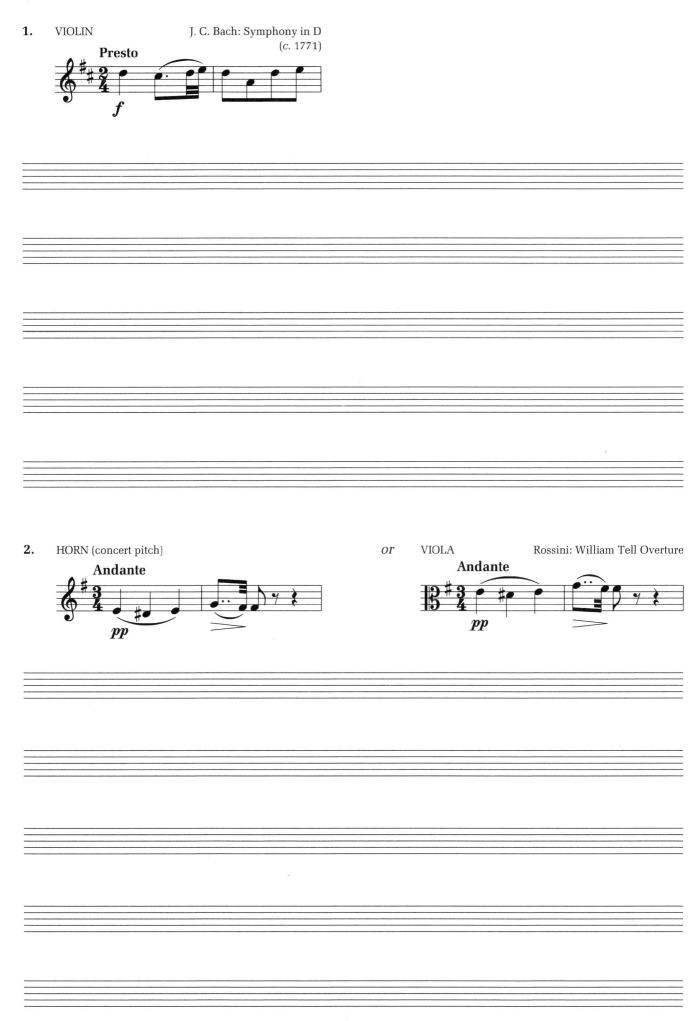

1.   VIOLIN   J. C. Bach: Symphony in D
                                        (*c.* 1771)

2.   HORN (concert pitch)   *or*   VIOLA   Rossini: William Tell Overture

3.   OBOE   Haydn: Piano Sonata in F, Hob. XVI:23

4.   DOUBLE BASS   *or* VIOLA   Berlioz: *Symphonie Fantastique*

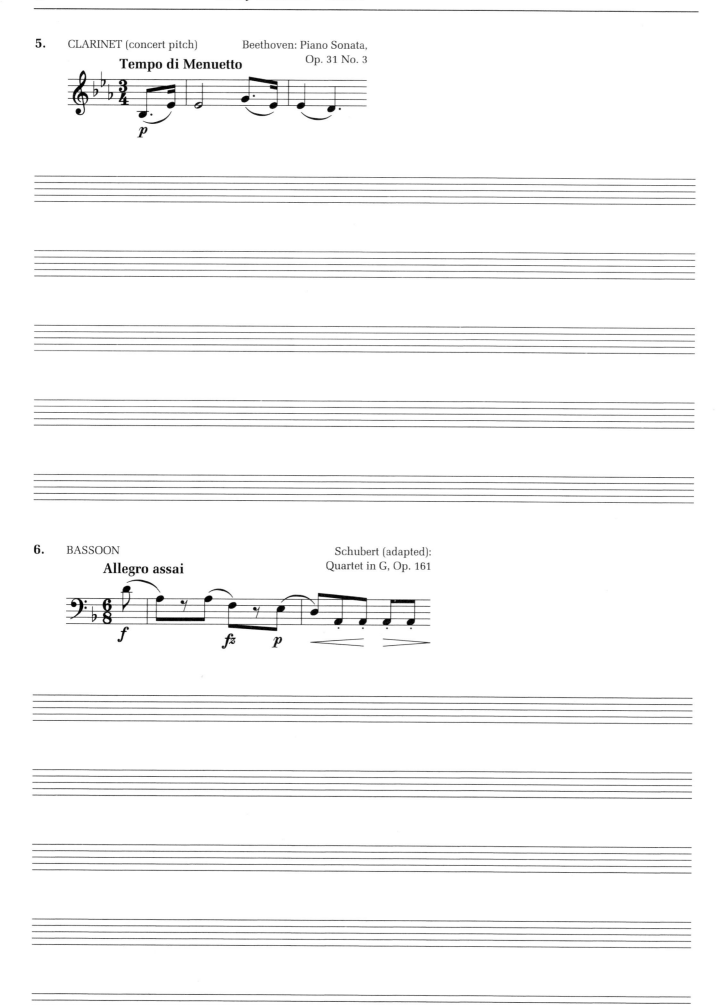

7. CELLO   Mozart (adapted):
    Tempo di Minuetto   Violin Sonata, K. 304

8. FLUTE   Weber: Piano Sonata, Op. 39 No. 3
    Allegro

Free-style melody

For the other, more modern, option, we will concentrate on writing for violin.

WORKING THE QUESTION

On studying the opening, we notice:

- the key seems to be C minor because of the key signature and the first two notes in particular;

- the melodic fall of a diminished 7th, a powerful interval;

- the dynamic/rhythmic contrast of two loud, accented crotchets and three fairly quiet, staccato quavers;

- the rhythm of an upbeat and a quaver rest, both of which will be relevant to the phrase structure;

- that all the notes are detached. We may therefore need some slurring for variety;

- that two of the notes are not in the key of C minor. The F♯ could be considered a decoration of the G, the dominant. The D♭ is less easy to describe as it is particularly foreign to the key and it is the last note of the given opening. It could be followed by C, and therefore treated as a decoration of the tonic.

There is clearly much opportunity presented in this opening, so now we will construct a 16-bar plan, which is the easiest for a balanced phrase structure.

Bar 1	2	3	4	5	6	7	8
Given opening	the note C	two-bar answering phrase using same rhythm		four-bar phrase using given rhythmic figures leading to imperfect cadence			

Bar 9	10	11	12	13	14	15	16
two-bar phrase modulating to subdominant		two-bar sequence to dominant		four-bar phrase using opening rhythmic figures and ending in tonic			

This plan has good structure and a plausible key scheme. Notice how the phrases overlap the bar-lines, so that we don't forget the all-important upbeat. Now for a first attempt to match this plan:

Moderato

This melody fits the plan well and has good phrase balance and tonal structure, but it could be much more imaginative in its development of the given motifs.

Our next version develops the melody along these lines:

Moderato

Notice how bars 3–4 (including the upbeat from bar 2) invert the shape of the opening phrase with the same rhythm, and use the violin's lowest note. The quavers in bars 5 and 6 now use the semitone as in the opening, before continuous quavers in bar 7 move on to the halfway cadence point. The F♯ decorates the G as the D♭ did the C in the opening. In bars 9–10 and 11–12 we use the opening rhythm and an inversion of the melodic shape in a more convincing modulating sequence; in 13–14 the opening rhythm is used again, and these bars include diminished intervals of a 4th, 5th and the important 7th before returning to the scale passage, which matches that in bar 7 and moves on to the final cadence.

The melodic writing is persistent in its rhythmic repetition and rather relentless and angry in character. But there is a sense of purpose and consistency about the line which we can now enhance with slurs, accents and other articulation, dynamic changes as in the given start, and some features which will make it look more like violin music, as shown at the top of the facing page. Note the powerful consecutive down bows and the final double-stop approached from the open G string. These features, specific to the instrument, require specialist knowledge, though for a good mark it is necessary only to write a melody as described in the opening of this section on page 39, and you should not worry if you do not have this knowledge.

Question 3   Sample Questions

The following practice questions can also be worked in different clefs and for other suitable instruments to extend their usefulness.

Compose melodies of not less than 12 bars using the following openings and for the given unaccompanied instruments. Continue in the same style and include appropriate performance directions.

1.   OBOE   Gavotta

2.   BASSOON

3.   HORN (concert pitch)   *or*   VIOLA

4.   CLARINET (concert pitch)

5.   CELLO

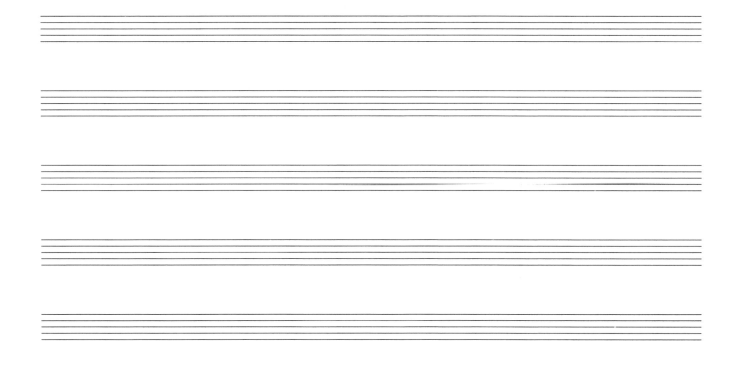

6.   TRUMPET (concert pitch)

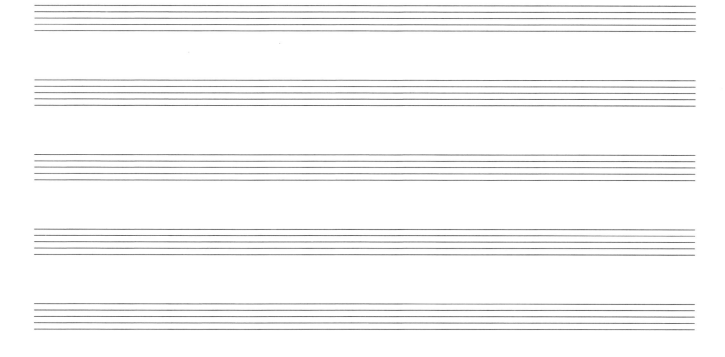

7.   FLUTE

Question 4

As in Grades 6 and 7, you will be given a passage of music and will be asked a number of questions which test your understanding of it. Though the syllabus statement remains the same for this question as it was for Grades 6 and 7, Grade 8 assumes a complete grasp of all the requirements for earlier grades plus knowledge of *all standard diatonic and chromatic chords.*

An awareness of motivic development is expected, together with a more extended knowledge of common structural, harmonic and contrapuntal devices. The ability to *apply* knowledge is also needed and it will be necessary to show powers of reasoning in answering questions which are not simply a matter of right or wrong (e.g. on style). This is particularly the case when the composer is not named. Keen musical perception and insight are required, particularly in recognising moods and effects, both instrumental and vocal.

A wide range of extracts is possible, using scores of up to four staves, but also including keyboard music on two staves. This smaller medium will normally be the most frequently used for questions on phrase structure because of the greater length of the extract. Transposing instruments and instruments that use a C clef may also be encountered.

Question 4   Sample Questions

Here are a number of tests such as you would find in an exam. The extracts chosen represent different nationalities and styles and some are well known, encouraging in-depth study with matching recordings. Some of the piano pieces have been set for ABRSM practical exams, and questions on these, and on similar extracts, will encourage greater understanding of what is being prepared for performance.

The first sample question includes a marks plan typical of that used in exams. In the remaining sample questions, the opportunity has been taken to exploit the extracts more fully, and more questions are asked than would be in a single exam. **Occasionally, in the exam, one slightly longer extract with questions worth a total of 50 marks may be used to cover the ground included in Questions 4 and 5.**

1. Study the extract printed opposite, which is taken from the Keyboard Sonata   [25]
Kp. 481 by Domenico Scarlatti, and then answer the questions below.

(a) Write out in full, as you think it should be played, the right-hand part of bar 2 (complete bar)
and bar 23 (last beat).

bar 2   bar 23

(4)

(b) Trace the key structure of the first 16 bars by completing the following statements:

The extract starts in the key of .... with a(n) .... cadence in that

key in bars 7–8. In bar 9 the key is .... with a decorated .... cadence

in bars .... Bars 13–14 modulate to the key of ...., and bars 15–16 to the

key of ....   (7)

(c) Mark clearly on the score, using the appropriate capital letter for identification, one example   (10)
of each of the following. Also give the bar numbers of your answers.

    A   a suspension forming a subdominant chord with 7th (iv^7)
       resolving on to the first inversion of a supertonic chord (ii°b) in F minor.   Bar ....

    B   the falling melodic interval of a diminished octave.   Bars ....

    C   a dominant 7th chord in second inversion (V^7c) with
       a suspended minor 9th above it, in the key of F minor.   Bar ....

    D   a bar **not** including syncopation between bars 13 and 19.   Bar ....

    E   a pedal point on the dominant of C minor (mark └———**E**———┘).   Bars ....

(d) In bar 4 draw a circle round each right-hand note which is unessential to the harmony and give
the name of these notes of melodic decoration.

        ....   (4)

2.   Study the extract from a string quartet printed opposite and then answer the questions below.

(a)   Trace the modulations in the opening section by naming the keys in the following bars:

bar 2   ....   bar 3   ....

bar 5   ....   bar 6   ....

bars 8–9   ....

(b)   Mark clearly on the score, using the appropriate capital letter for identification, one example of each of the following. Also give the bar numbers of your answers.

A   the melodic interval of an augmented octave in the viola part.   Bars ....

B   a chromatic note of anticipation.   Bar ....

C   a chromatic rising appoggiatura.   Bar ....

D   a 9–8 suspension between viola and second violin.   Bars ....

E   an appoggiatura over dominant 7th harmony.   Bar ....

(c)   Identify the chords marked * in bars 10, 13 and 14 by writing on the dotted lines below. Use either words or symbols. State the position of each chord, whether it is major, minor, augmented or diminished, and give the prevailing key of each.

bar 10   ....   bar 13   ....

bar 14   ....

(d)   Answer TRUE or UNTRUE to each of the following statements:

(i)   The viola sounds the lowest note of the four instruments in only one bar.   ....

(ii)   The second violin sounds the highest note played.   ....

(iii) The harmonic interval between the cello and viola on the fourth quaver of bar 13 is a compound major 6th.   ....

(e)   Complete the following statements:

The texture and movement of the parts in bars 1–5 is mainly .... whereas in bars 6–9 the music is more .... The climax of the extract is in bar(s) .... and it is achieved by a gradual .... in bars ...., the use of a repeated rhythm with changing harmony in the three lower instruments of bar ...., and .... rhythm in the first violin part of bar ....

(f)   Underline the name of the likely composer from the list below:

Bartók   Haydn   Mendelssohn   Purcell

Give the reasons for your choice.

....

....

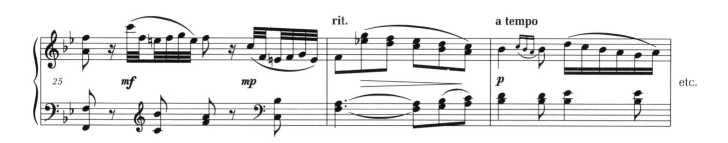

3.   Study the second movement from the Sonata in F for piano by Dušek (1731–1799), printed opposite and above, and then answer the following questions. (Dynamics, phrasing and marks of articulation are not by the composer, but are all editorial.)

(a)   Mark clearly on the score, using the appropriate capital letter for identification, one example of each of the following. Also give the bar numbers of your answers.

A   a pair of chromatic lower auxiliary notes in 3rds, one in each hand.   Bar ....

B   the progression Ic–V^7–I in the **dominant** key.   Bar ....

C   an extended diminished 7th broken chord in G minor.   Bar ....

D   a dominant 9th in the **second part** of the extract.   Bar ....

E   a short sequence within one bar which passes through the key of the supertonic minor.

   Bar ....

F   the harmonic interval of a diminished 4th between two left-hand notes.   Bar ....

(b)   Complete the following statements:

The theme and harmony used in bars 18–21 were first heard in bars .... but now the key

is .... There are modulations to the key of .... in bars 22–23, to

.... in bar 23, and to .... in bars 24–25 before returning to

the key of .... for the return of the opening, starting in bar ....

(c)   Look at bars 17–19 and, in these bars, draw a numbered circle around the following examples of notes of melodic decoration in the right-hand part:

①   an accented passing note

②   an appoggiatura

(d)   Answer **TRUE** or **UNTRUE** to each of the following statements:

(i)   All the notes in the right hand of bar 5 are essential to the harmony.   ....

(ii)   The chord in the second half of bar 6 is a dominant 7th in first inversion.   ....

(iii)   In bar 17, the right-hand part contains all the notes of the top half of a melodic minor scale,

ascending and descending.   ....

(iv)   The right-hand note C in bar 21 is a changing note.   ....

(v)   The notes and rhythm in bars 6–7 are different from bars 8–9, but the harmony is the same.

....

Allegretto non troppo, capriccioso

4.   Study the extract from the piano piece *Children's Quarrelling at Play* from *Pictures at an Exhibition* by Mussorgsky, printed opposite and above, and then answer the following questions.

(a)   Mark clearly on the score, using the appropriate capital letter for identification, one example of each of the following. Also give the bar numbers of your answers.

   A   a chromatic lower auxiliary note in bars 1–4.   Bar ....

   B   a pedal point on the dominant of G major in bars 14–21 (mark ⌊____B____⌋).   Bars ....

   C   an augmented 6th chord between bars 16 and 20.   Bar ....

(b)   Identify the chords marked * in bars 14, 15 and 16 by writing on the dotted lines below. Use either words or symbols. State the position of each chord, whether it is major, minor, augmented or diminished, and give the prevailing key of each.

   bar 14 ....   bar 15 ....

   bar 16 ....

(c)   Show the phrase structure by drawing phrase marks above the right-hand part of bars 1–13.

(d)   Complete the following statements:

   Mussorgsky achieves the contrast between bars 14–19 and the opening section (bars 1–13) by making

   bars 14–19 more .... and more ...., having less active

   .... and a slower rate of .... change. The .... is

   more close-knit, frequently with .... movement in the lowest part. The harmony

   is mainly .... key and .... in mood coming after an abrupt ending to the

   preceding happy .... key section.

(e)   The melodic intervals marked **1–4** in the top line of the right hand of bars 17–18 are:

   1.   ....

   2.   ....

   3.   ....

   4.   ....

(f)   Describe two features of the piano writing which reflect the title of the piece.

   1.   ....

   2.   ....

5. Study the extract from a prelude for piano called *Minstrels*, printed opposite, and then answer the questions below.

(a) Give the meaning of each of the following:

Modéré   ....

les "gruppetti" (grace notes) *sur le temps* (bar 1)   ....

Cédez . . // Mouvt. (bars 4–5)   ....

très détaché (bar 9)   ....

⌃ (bar 18)   ....

(b) Complete the following statements:

(i)   In the first four bars, the melodic interval of a diminished 4th does **not** appear in bar ....

(ii) A pentatonic scale provides the notes for the four bars from bar .... to bar ....

(iii) The chord on the last quaver of bar 13 is ....

(iv) Bar .... shows the progression V–I in F♯ major.

(v)   The interval between the top and bottom notes of bar 17, beat 1, is a(n) ....

(c) Name **four** ways in which the character and style of the extract depict the humour asked for by the composer.

1.   ....

2.   ....

3.   ....

4.   ....

(d) In the first half of bar 14 circle and number two pairs of notes of melodic decoration, giving their names.

①   ....

②   ....

(e) Describe briefly the texture of the first eight bars and that of bars 13–18.

Bars 1–8   ....

Bars 13–18   ....

(f) Underline the name of the likely composer from the list below:

Berlioz   Bizet   Franck   Debussy

Give **three** reasons for your choice.

1.   ....

2.   ....

3.   ....

attacca

6. Study the extract for piano trio, printed opposite and above, and then answer the following questions.

(a) Give the meaning of each of the following:

Langsam, mit inniger Empfindung ....

attacca (bar 15) ....

(b) Identify the chords marked * in bars 4, 5, 10 and 15 by writing on the dotted lines below. Use either words or symbols. Also for bar 4 state the position, whether it is major, minor, augmented or diminished, and the prevailing key.

bar 4 .... key ....

bar 5 ....

bar 10 ....

bar 15 ....

(c) Mark clearly on the score, using the appropriate capital letter for identification, one example of each of the following. Also give the bar numbers of your answers.

A the melodic interval of a diminished 3rd in the cello part. Bar ....

B the harmonic interval of a compound diminished 7th between the string parts. Bar ....

C an augmented triad in the piano part. Bar ....

D an upward resolving chromatic appoggiatura in the piano part. Bar ....

E a pedal point on the mediant in the key of D minor (mark └_____E_____┘). Bars ....

F an interrupted cadence. Bar(s) ....

G three successive augmented 6th chords (Italian, French, German) in one bar of the piano part, between bar 10 and the end of the extract (mark ┌_____G_____┐). Bar ....

(Turn the page)

(d) Complete the following statements:

(i) The key at the start is ...., though in bar 3 the music modulates through

.... before returning to the opening key in bar .... Bar 6 suggests the key of

.... but once again a return to the initial key is made in the following bar. The

only perfect cadence (a decorated one) in the extract is in the key of .... in bar

.... The extract ends on a(n) .... cadence in the key of ....

(ii) In the last four bars of the right-hand piano part, there is a harmonic interval of a diminished

4th on the .... beat of bar ...., and a melodic interval of a diminished 4th in bar ....

The harmonic interval between the cello and violin at the start of the last beat of bar 12 is a(n)

....

(e) Describe the thematic connection between the violin part in bars 1–5 and the right-hand piano part
from bar 9 onwards by completing the following statements:

The .... and shape are the same, though the piano part has more ....

The piano part mainly relates to the key of .... whereas the violin part relates to the

key of ....

(f) Underline one period during which you think this music was composed:

          1650–1750   1750–1800   1800–1900   1900–1950

Give reasons for your choice and suggest the name of a possible composer.

....

....

....

....

Question 5

As in Grades 6 and 7, you will be given a passage of music and will be asked a number of questions which test your understanding of it. Though the syllabus statement remains the same for this question as it was for Grades 6 and 7, Grade 8 assumes a complete grasp of all the requirements for earlier grades plus knowledge of *all standard diatonic and chromatic chords.*

An awareness of motivic development, together with a more extended knowledge of common structural, harmonic and contrapuntal devices, is expected, as is the ability to *apply* knowledge in reasoned answers which are not simply a matter of right or wrong (e.g. on style). This is particularly the case when the composer is not named. Keen musical perception and insight are required, particularly in recognising moods and effects, both instrumental and vocal.

Extracts used may be taken from opera, oratorio or scores for orchestra. However, there is no *requirement* that large forces must be used and some vocal extracts may have the orchestral part reduced for piano.

A working knowledge of standard Italian, German and French musical terms, names of instruments and instructions to players is expected, though English scores and terminology may also appear. The ability to transpose will also be tested.

Question 5 Sample Questions

Here are a number of tests such as you would find in an exam. The extracts chosen represent different nationalities, styles and performing resources and some are well known, encouraging in-depth study with matching recordings.

The first sample question includes a marks plan typical of that used in exams. In the remaining sample questions, the opportunity has been taken to exploit the extracts more fully, and more questions are asked than would be in a single exam. **Occasionally, in the exam, one slightly longer extract with questions worth a total of 50 marks may be used to cover the ground included in Questions 4 and 5.**

1. Study the short extract from the second movement of Walton's Second Symphony, printed below, and then answer the questions which follow.

(a) For each of the following signs and terms, (1) give its meaning, and $\boxed{25}$
      (2) describe the effect it would have on the sound produced.

+

fp $>$ 1. ....
(first horn, bar 4)
               2. .... (2)

○
♩   1. ....
(harp, bar 4)
               2. .... (2)

div. con sord   1. ....
(violins, bar 5)
               2. .... (2)

p dim. niente   1. ....
(violins, bars 5–7)
               2. .... (2)

(b) Write out the first four bars as they would sound at concert pitch for:

corno inglese   (2)

first clarinet   (1)

bass clarinet   (2)

first bassoon   (1)

first horn   (2)

(c) In bar 5, circle any notes which are enharmonic equivalents of the first violin notes.   (2)

(d) (i) Describe how the first four bars for first bassoon are melodically constructed.

        ....

        .... (3)

   (ii) How do the entries for bass clarinet and corno inglese relate to these opening four bars?

        ....

        .... (2)

   (iii) Identify the chord played by strings in bar 5, naming the key, the position of the chord
        and whether it is major, minor, augmented or diminished. Use either words or symbols.

        .... (2)

69

2.   Study the opening bars of Rossini's Overture from *The Barber of Seville*, printed on pages 71–72, and then answer the questions below.

(a)   Give the meaning of:

Gran Tamburo   ....

a 2 (bassoon, bar 1)   ....

1. (oboe, bar 6)   ....

𝄽 (viola, bar 7)   ....

(b)   Apart from horns and trumpets, two instruments in this extract do not sound at the written pitch. Name them, and state the direction and interval of transposition from the written note for each.

1.   ....

2.   ....

(c)   Identify the four chords played by the strings in bars 6–7 by writing on the dotted lines below. Use either words or symbols, and give the prevailing key for the first three chords.

bar 6   ....   and   ...., both chords in the key of ....

bar 7   ....   in the key of ....   and   ....

(d)   Describe how Rossini varies the first five bars by completing the following statements:

Two very loud chords on the tonic are followed by quiet repeated notes which outline a rising

.... figure, played by .... and .... Woodwind then modulate to the key

of .... in bar 2 and the same modulation is echoed by .... a(n) .... lower

in bars 2–3. The whole two and a half bar pattern is then repeated, but this time starting with a pair

of loud chords on the .... and ending in the .... key in bar 5.

(e)   Write out the parts as they would sound at concert pitch for horns and trumpets in bar 1 and bar 3. Use the appropriate key signature.

(f)   Mark clearly on the score, using the appropriate capital letter for identification, one example of each of the following. Also give the bar numbers of your answers.

A   a triple stop which is a second inversion of a dominant chord.   Bar ....

B   the harmonic interval of an augmented 5th between two of the same instruments.   Bar ....

C   the melodic interval of a diminished 4th.   Bar ....

(g)   Name two features of the extract which create the 'maestoso' quality that Rossini indicates.

1.   ....

2.   ....

3. Study the extract from Bloch's *Schelomo* ('Solomon', Hebraic Rhapsody for solo cello and large orchestra), printed on pages 74–75, and then answer the questions below.

(a) Give the meaning of:

Tamburo   ....

Tambour de Basque   ....

Viola (al meno 8)   ....

3 Soli con sord. (first violins, bar 1)   ....

(b) (i)   Name each of the following harmonic intervals:

   1. between the bassoons in bar 1, beat 3   ....

   2. between the clarinets in bar 9, last quaver   ....

(ii)   Name each of the melodic intervals marked **W**, **X**, **Y** and **Z** in the solo cello part of bars 7–8:

bar 7, **W** ....   bar 8, **X** ....

bar 8, **Y** ....   bar 8, **Z** ....

(c) Which instrument(s):

(i)   plays the same notes as the first violins in bar 1 an octave lower?   ....

(ii)   sound the same notes as the first and second clarinets in bar 3?   ....

(iii) sounds an octave lower than written?   ....

(d) Answer **TRUE** or **UNTRUE** to each of the following statements:

(i)   Bar 2 of the viola part has one more pitch than bar 1.   ....

(ii)   The celeste part in bars 1–2 consists entirely of major triads in second inversion.   ....

(iii) All solo cello notes in bar 7 belong to one or other form of the scale of A minor.   ....

(e) (i)   How is the theme for violas in bar 3 used and developed in bars 4–6?

   ....

   ....

   ....

   ....

(ii)   How is the theme for solo cello in bar 7 developed in bars 8–9 in the same part?

   ....

   ....

   ....

   ....

(f) Underline one set of words in each of the following pairs which best describes the music:

(i)   EITHER   contrapuntal (polyphonic) texture   OR   single melody line with harmony

(ii)   EITHER   chromatic melodic lines   OR   diatonic melodic lines

(iii) EITHER   regular, metrical rhythm   OR   rhapsodic rhythm

(iv)   EITHER   the key in bar 1 is G minor   OR   the music of bar 1 is atonal

Reproduced by permission of G. Schirmer Ltd on behalf of G. Schirmer, Inc.

4.   Study the extract printed opposite and then answer the questions below. The orchestral part is reduced to a piano score.

(a) Trace the modulations by naming the keys, giving bar numbers.

....

....

....

(b) Mark clearly on the score, using the appropriate capital letter for identification, one example of each of the following. Also give the bar numbers of your answers.

   A   an upward chromatic appoggiatura.   Bar ....

   B   a simultaneous pair of notes of anticipation in the vocal parts.   Bar ....

   C   the start of a two-bar harmonic sequence a note lower than the original two bars.   Bar ....

   D   a diminished 7th chord in the orchestral reduction.   Bar ....

   E   a Ic–V^7 progression above the dominant note in the orchestral reduction.   Bar ....

   F   the third inversion of a dominant 7th chord in the key of E♭ major.   Bar ....

   G   a chromatic lower auxiliary note in the orchestral reduction.   Bar ....

(c) Identify the chords marked * in bars 4, 6 and 14 by writing on the dotted lines below. Use either words or symbols. Also for bar 6 state the position, whether it is major, minor, augmented or diminished and the prevailing key.

   bar 4   ....

   bar 6   ....   key ....

   bar 14   ....

(d) Write out the top line of bar 15 of the orchestral reduction as you think it should be played.

(e) Answer **TRUE** or **UNTRUE** to each of the following statements:

   (i)   The choral writing is mainly homophonic.   ....

   (ii) The material in the opening phrase does not appear again.   ....

   (iii) The interval between the lowest and highest notes of the orchestral reduction **right-hand part** in bar 3 is a compound perfect 5th.   ....

   (iv) There are no unaccented passing notes in the vocal parts.   ....

(f) Name the period during which the piece was composed, and suggest a possible composer, giving reasons for your choice.

....

....

....

....

5.   Study the operatic extract printed opposite and on page 80, and then answer the questions below.

(a) (i)   Give the English names for:

Bratsche   ....

Posaunen (bar 14)   ....

Pauken (bar 14)   ....

(ii)   Give the meaning of:

Mässig langsam, ohne zu schleppen   ....

ausdrucksvoll (bar 1)   ....

Fis (Pauken, bar 14)   ....

(b) (i)   Identify **five** places where the composer develops the motif ![motif] (bars 4–5) during the rest of the extract in the instrumental parts. Give the instruments and bar numbers concerned.

1.   instrument(s) .... bar(s) ....

2.   instrument(s) .... bar(s) ....

3.   instrument(s) .... bar(s) ....

4.   instrument(s) .... bar(s) ....

5.   instrument(s) .... bar(s) ....

(ii)   Another important motif is developed by the lower strings in this extract. Give the bar numbers and the name of the pair of woodwind instruments who join them in a rhythmically and melodically altered version of it.

bars   ....   instrument   ....

(c)   Write out the parts for Englisches Horn, 3 Klarinetten and Bass Klarinette as they would sound at concert pitch in bars 10–11, using the appropriate key signature. Use the staves and clefs given at the foot of page 80, or use a separate sheet of manuscript paper.

(d)   Complete the following statements:

(i)   The chord played by the trombones and tuba in bar 15 is a   ....

(ii)   The key at the start of the extract is .... and at the end it is ....

(iii)   There is an enharmonic change in the .... violins between bars .... and ....

(iv)   The chord played by the strings in bar 19 is a   ....

(e)   Name **four** ways in which the composer ensures that the vocal line is heard through the orchestra.

1.   ....

2.   ....

3.   ....

4.   ....

(f)   Name a likely composer, giving the reasons for your choice.

....

....

6. Study the extract from *The Sorcerer's Apprentice* by Dukas, printed on pages 81–83, and then answer the questions on pages 83–84.

(a) **(i)** Give the meaning of each of the following terms:

Assez lent ....

léger (flutes, bar 2) ....

sons ordinaires (harp, bar 5) ....

Vif (bar 14) ....

1er **mouv**.^t (bar 18) ....

◊ (first violin, bar 18) ....

(ii) Give the English names of the following instruments:

Petite flûte ....   Alto ....

(b) Answer TRUE or UNTRUE to each of the following statements:

(i) The highest-sounding note on the first beat of bar 14 is played by the first flute. ....

(ii) The only note played by the horns in bar 14 which is not doubled at the same pitch in the violin parts is the written note C played by the third horn. ....

(iii) All the notes played by the clarinets in bar 16 sound an octave lower than those in the flutes. ....

(iv) The chord in the violins in bar 14 is a dominant 7th with minor 9th in C minor. ....

(v) The trumpet parts are written for Trumpets in A. ....

(vi) In bar 8 the petite flûte plays the note E♮ three times. ....

(Turn the page)

(c) **(i)** Here is the clarinet part of bars 3–4. Write it out as it would sound at concert pitch. Use the appropriate key signature.

(ii) Show where this theme, or part of it, is used during the rest of the extract by giving the bar numbers and instruments concerned in **five** examples of its use.

1. instrument .... bars ....

2. instrument .... bars ....

3. instrument .... bars ....

4. instrument .... bars ....

5. instrument .... bars ....

(d) Mark clearly on the score, using the appropriate capital letter for identification, one example of each of the following. Also give the bar numbers of your answers.

A   a plucked, quadruple stop played without mutes.   Bar ....

B   a fast scale passage built on the enharmonic equivalent notes of B major.   Bar ....

C   the harmonic interval of an augmented 5th played twice in succession between two of the same woodwind instruments.   Bar ....

D   an augmented triad played by the harp.   Bar ....

(e) Name **four** ways in which the theme played by the solo horn in bars 20–22 differs from the solo flute in bars 18–20.

1. ....

2. ....

3. ....

4. ....

(f) The composer creates a mysterious atmosphere in bars 1–13 of this extract. Describe how he does this by completing the following statements:

The tempo is ...., with eerie, unusual chords such as the .... triad

played by the woodwind on the first beat of bar 8. .... are used for lower strings and

harp, and it is very .... in dynamics. The tone of the violins is affected by the use of

........................, making their sound ...., while the lower strings anchor the harmony

with a .... which sounds throughout these bars.

Answers to Question 4

These are specimen answers. Alternative responses are often possible, and will receive credit if they accurately answer part of or the full requirements of the question.

1. (a)

bar 2 *(other versions possible)*   bar 23 *(other versions possible)*

   (b) F minor; imperfect; A♭ major; perfect; 11–12; E♭ major; C minor

   (c) **A** bar 5, beat 1   **B** bars 9–10 *or* bars 11–12
       C bar 6, beat 3   **D** bar 17   **E** bars 18–20

   (d) third E♮ and B♭;   appoggiatura

2. (a) bar 2: A♭ major   bar 3: E♭ major   bar 5: G minor
       bar 6: C minor   bars 8–9: E♭ major

   (b) **A** bars 13–14   **B** F♯, Vln.1, bar 4   **C** E♮, Vln.1, bar 10
       D bars 7–8   **E** E♭, Vln.1, bar 8

   (c) bar 10: V^7c (major) in E♭ major
       bar 13: ivb (minor) in E♭ minor *or* iv$^{♭3}$b (minor) in E♭ major
       bar 14: vii$^{(dim)7}$ (diminished) in B♭ minor

   (d) **(i)** UNTRUE   **(ii)** TRUE   **(iii)** TRUE

   (e) homophonic *or* chordal;   contrapuntal *or* polyphonic *or* linear; 13–14 *or* 14;   crescendo;   11–12;   13;   syncopated;   13

   (f) Mendelssohn (String Quartet No. 1 in E♭, Op. 12)
       harmony is chromatic in a Romantic style, too rich for Purcell or Haydn, but not dissonant enough for Bartók;
       music is tonal, but modulations are too frequent and too diverse for Purcell or Haydn

3. (a) **A** bar 12, third quaver   **B** bar 11 *or* bar 13
      C bar 14, left hand   **D** bar 26, second quaver
      E bar 3   **F** bar 10, third quaver

   (b) 1–4;   E♭ major;   C minor;   B♭ major;
       F major;   B♭ major;   27

   (c) ① E♮, bar 17   ② G, bar 18

   (d) **(i)** TRUE   **(ii)** UNTRUE   **(iii)** UNTRUE
      (iv) TRUE   **(v)** TRUE

4. (a) **A** C𝄪 in bar 2 *or* bar 4   **B** bars 20–21   **C** bar 18, third beat

   (b) bar 14: i (minor) in D♯ minor
       bar 15: ib+$^{♯6}$ (minor) in B minor
       bar 16: V^{13} (major) in C♯ major

   (c) five two-bar phrases followed by one three-bar phrase

   (d) legato *or* smooth;   melodic *or* lyrical *or* continuous;
       rhythm;   harmonic;   harmony *or* texture;
       chromatic *or* semitone;   minor;   sad;   major

   (e) 1. perfect 5th   2. perfect 4th   3. diminished 5th
      4. chromatic semitone *or* augmented unison

   (f) 1. repetitions of lively figures, both rhythmic and harmonic
      2. frequent contrast of slurred chords and staccato semiquavers

5. (a) at a moderate speed;   the grace notes on the beat;
relax the speed, then original tempo;
very detached;   an accented short note

(b) (i) 4   **(ii)** 8;   11
(iii) supertonic 7th in first inversion (ii^{7}b) *or*
subdominant (root position) with added 6th (IV^6)
(iv) 18   **(v)** augmented 4th

(c) use of grace-notes repeatedly; sudden dynamic changes; tempo
changes; 'drumming' effects of consecutive 2nds; use of staccato;
surprising harmony from bar 16 to the end of the extract

(d) ① F♯ and D: unaccented passing notes
② D and B: lower auxiliary notes

(e) nearly all single line – very sparse (monophonic);
much thicker – harmonised in up to seven parts (chordal)

(f) Debussy
two tempo changes within the first nine bars;
frequent dynamic and articulation changes;
pentatonic scale;   chords with added notes;
jazz influences rule out other composers

6. (a) slow, with heartfelt (sincere) expression;   go straight on

(b) bar 4:   Neapolitan 6th ($^♭$IIb, major) in A minor *or*
VIb (major) in D minor
bar 5:   German (augmented) 6th
bar 10:   Italian (augmented) 6th
bar 15:   French (augmented) 6th

(c) A   bar 4, beats 3–4   **B**   bar 5, beat 2   **C**   bar 9
D   bar 4, F✗ *or* bar 5, F✗ *or* bar 12, B♯ *or* bar 13, D♯
E   bars 9–10   **F**   bar 2 *or* bars 2–3 *or* bars 4–5 *or* bars 8–9
G   bar 13, first minim

(d) (i) A minor;   D minor;   5;   E minor;
G minor;   11;   imperfect;   D minor
(ii) fourth;   12;   14;   compound augmented 2nd

(e) rhythm;   rests;   D minor;   A minor

(f) 1800–1900;   Schumann (Piano Trio, Op. 63)
thick, low textures;
rich harmonic vocabulary, but clearly tonal;
initial speed direction in German

Answers to Question 5

These are specimen answers. Alternative responses are often possible, and will receive credit if they accurately answer part of or the full requirements of the question.

1. **(a)** 1. hand-stopped and blown hard, loud but immediately, suddenly quiet, then getting still quieter
       2. initially a hard, brassy effect but then getting thinner in tone
       1. harmonic
       2. the actual sound would be an octave higher than the written note, and quiet with a pure or bell-like tone
       1. violins 1 and 2 are each divided into two parts and are to use mutes
       2. this makes the tone muffled but sweet and quiet
       1. quiet, getting quieter, nothing
       2. the dynamic is to fade gradually from quiet to nothing at all

   (b)

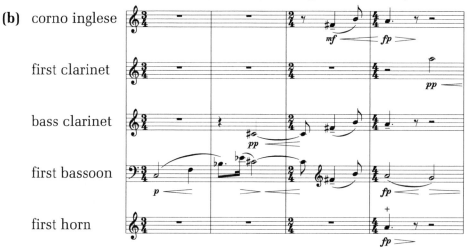

corno inglese

first clarinet

bass clarinet

first bassoon

first horn

   (c) harp B♭ and C♭ (and clarinet written C♯)
   (d) **(i)** built on rising 4ths, falling a sounding tone in bars 2 and 4
       (ii) they are in unison with the bassoon;
           they therefore add tone colour and volume to the crescendo
       (iii) I⁷c (major) in B major

2. **(a)** bass drum;   both players play the same notes;
       first player only;
       each minim is played as eight repeated semiquavers

   (b) 1. piccolo, sounds an octave higher than the written note
       2. double bass, sounds an octave lower than the written note

   (c) i;   V⁷b;   C♯ minor;   V⁷c;   A major;   German (augmented) 6th
   (d) scale;   strings;   bassoons;   F♯ minor;
       strings;   octave;   dominant;   tonic

   (e) horns

       trumpets

   (f) **A** bar 3, beat 3 (first violins)
       B bar 4, last semiquaver (oboes *or* clarinets) *or*
           bar 5, beat 2, last semiquaver (violins)

          C   bar 4, last beat (flute *or* first oboe *or* first clarinet) *or*
                  bar 5, beat 2 (first violins)

  (g) fortissimo repeated chords (tutti) at start and in bar 3 on I and V;
        use of trumpets and drums; slow pace

3. (a) (snare) drum;   tambourine;
        violas, at least 8 (players);   3 solo players, muted

  (b) (i) 1.   minor 9th *or* compound minor 2nd   2.   augmented 4th
      (ii) **W**   minor 3rd
             X   chromatic semitone *or* augmented unison
             Y   diminished 4th   **Z**   augmented 2nd

  (c) (i) celeste   **(ii)** bassoons 1 and 2   **(iii)** double bass

  (d) (i) TRUE   **(ii)** UNTRUE   **(iii)** TRUE

  (e) (i) repeated by violas in bar 4 but with diminution of rhythm at
        end of bar (creating a three-beat bar); then played a 4th lower
        by flute and oboe in bars 5–6, with a longer final note
    (ii) first three notes are repeated at beginning of bar 8, then the
        theme becomes more decorated, with shorter note values, and
        it becomes higher in pitch; in bar 9 the opening two notes of
        the theme are repeated in a rising sequence

  (f) (i) single melody line with harmony
    (ii) chromatic melodic lines
    (iii) rhapsodic rhythm   **(iv)** the key in bar 1 is G minor

4. (a) After starting in B♭ major, the extract modulates to C minor in bars
        5–7, and returns to B♭ major for bars 8–12. The music passes
        briefly through E♭ major in bars 13–14 then, after a chromatic
        passage, B♭ major is reached on the second beat of bar 15.

  (b) **A**   B♮ in bar 2 (*or* bar 13) *or* F♯ in bar 5
      B   bar 11, last semiquaver   **C**   bar 8
      D   bar 14, last semiquaver *or* bar 15, beat 1
      E   bar 15, beats 2–3   **F** bar 13, beat 3   **G** bar 3, last quaver

  (c) German (augmented) 6th;   V^{7}d (major) in C minor;
      Italian (augmented) 6th

  (d)  *(other versions possible)*

  (e) (i) TRUE   **(ii)** UNTRUE   **(iii)** UNTRUE   **(iv)** UNTRUE
  (f) Classical;   Haydn (Mass in B♭ major, *Harmoniemesse*)
      (Mozart, Beethoven, Schubert and contemporaries also possible)
      Homophonic writing for choir, preponderance of regular phrasing,
      melody-dominated texture, ornamentation, melodic decoration
      and clear-cut cadences using the cadential second inversion all
      point to the Classical period.

5. (a) (i) viola;   trombones;   timpani (kettle drums)
       (ii) moderately slow, without dragging;   expressively;   F♯

  (b) (i) first oboe, first violins; bars 7–8
        first clarinet, first violins; bars 10–11
        second oboe, cor anglais, first clarinet; bars 12–13
        first violins; bar 13
        first oboe, cor anglais, first clarinet, first violins; bar 14
        first violins; bars 18–19
    (ii) 11–14;   bassoons

(c)   Englisches
           Horn

           3 Klarinetten

           Bass
           Klarinette

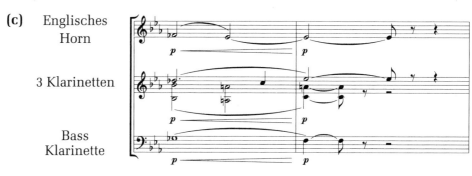

(d) (i) diminished 7th   **(ii)** E minor;   B (major *or* minor)
     (iii) second; 18 and 19   **(iv)** dominant 7th

(e) orchestral dynamics mainly quiet;   low-pitch accompaniment;
         vocal part almost always higher than orchestra; very little brass;
         vocal line usually more rhythmically active than instruments;
         start and finish both have small accompanying forces

(f) Wagner (*Götterdämmerung*)
         chromatic harmony; discords resolve on to other discords with a
         lack of conventional cadence points; strong use of (leit)motif;
         reedy textures (with bass clarinet, cor anglais, etc.);
         opera in German language and German terms;
         extensive use of sequential writing

6. (a) (i) sufficiently (*or* quite) slow *or* slow enough *or* very slow;
                light;   natural sounds (i.e. not harmonics);
                quick or lively;   original tempo;   (artificial) harmonic
                (shows where the finger should lightly touch the string)
       (ii) piccolo;   viola

   (b) (i) UNTRUE   **(ii)** TRUE   **(iii)** TRUE
       (iv) TRUE   **(v)**   UNTRUE   **(vi)** UNTRUE

   (c) (i)

       (ii) harp; bars 3–6
                first oboe; bars 4–5
                first flute; bars 5–6
                harp; bars 9–12
                first clarinet; bars 9–10
                first oboe; bars 10–11
                first flute; bars 11–12
                first trumpet; bars 17–18

   (d) A bar 14, second violins   **B** bar 16, harp
       C bar 16, beats 2–3, oboes   **D** bar 22

   (e) 1. the horn is a minor 6th lower (C major not A♭ major)
           2. it jumps to the normal major 3rd of the scale, not the flat 3rd
           3. it is very quiet throughout, instead of starting loud and getting
               quiet
           4. the last note of the horn part is longer

   (f) slow;   augmented;   harmonics;   quiet;
            mutes;   muffled *or* sweet *or* quiet;   pedal